ZODIAC

LOTHIAN

Edited by Steve Twelvetree

First published in Great Britain in 2002 by
YOUNG WRITERS
Remus House,
Coltsfoot Drive,
Peterborough, PE2 9JX
Telephone (01733) 890066

HB ISBN 0 75433 698 0
SB ISBN 0 75433 699 9

FOREWORD

Young Writers was established in 1991 with the aim of promoting creative writing in children, to make reading and writing poetry fun.

Once again, this year proved to be a tremendous success with over 41,000 entries received nationwide.

The Zodiac competition has shown us the high standard of work and effort that children are capable of today. The competition has given us a vivid insight into the thoughts and experiences of today's younger generation. It is a reflection of the enthusiasm and creativity that teachers have injected into their pupils, and it shines clearly within this anthology.

The task of selecting poems was a difficult one, but nevertheless, an enjoyable experience. We hope you are as pleased with the final selection in *Zodiac Lothian* as we are.

CONTENTS

Alan Rooney	109
Jamie Fairley	110
Stacey Burns	111
Leah Kelly	112
Ami Reid	113
Ian Munro	114
Jemma Gilchrist	115

Merchiston Castle School

Michael Ashby	116
Jonathan Paterson	117
Matthew Hardcastle	118
Neil Campbell	120
Andrew Knox	122
Oliver Rodi	123
Michael Black	124
Adam Clark	125
Alasdair Hardie	126
Archie Millar	127
Hamish Locke	128
Alastair Hall	129
James Valpy	130
Jon Watson	131
Josh Deery	132
Jonathan Gemmell	133
James B Arbuthnott	134
Leo J H Collins	135
Farooq Javed	136
Lewis Deaves	137
Peter Singh	138
Charles Costello	139
James Henderson	140

Newbattle Community High School

Shelley McHale	141
Emma MacInnes	142
Callum McLean	143
Gary McNaughton	144

Nathan Rutherford	145
Shaun McNeish	146
Stacey McCue	147
Colin Haddow	148
Louise Wilson	149
Neal Trainer	150
Kerry Walker	151
Callum Smith	152
Samantha Ray	153
Kelly Pryde	154
Daniel Stuart	155
Robyn O'Brien	156

St David's High School, Dalkeith
| Bryan Monaghan | 157 |

Whitburn Acadamy
Jamie Doyle	158
Mark Peebles	159
Kathryn Graham	160
Stephen Kyle	161
Teirnie Miller	162
Samantha Kellock	163
Lynsay McShane	164
Diane Malcolm	165
Stuart Wright	166
Steven McCallum	167
Pamela Johnston	168
Cheryl Fawcett	169
Elaine Mill	170
Angela Bonnar	171
Nancy Cook	172
Nikki Sked	173
Billy Sharp	174
Lynne Charge	175
Gary McKenzie	176
Amy Stewart	177
David Paterson	178

The Poems

THE LAND OF THE WOLF

The river snakes through the wood;
The mist forms a grey-black hood;
The wolf's howls come through the trees
And echoing them howls the freezing breeze;
The rocks rear up to mountains tall,
And on them snow will always fall.
No king could ever rule this land;
It is ruled by nature's royal hand.

Eystein Thanisch (13)

DAN, DAN, THE WAFFLE MAN!

Baked one day in an oven so hot, that awful waffle, will he
                                        ever get caught?
Ready to be taken out, crispy brown. Took a look about and
                                        started to frown.
'Open this door, open this door!'
He cried, 'It's getting really hot
Hurry, hurry, I'm not asking a lot.'

The man baking the waffle took a good listen,
Panicked, he nearly had kittens!
'Oh no, oh no. What have I done?
There is a little boy trapped in my oven!'

He rushed the oven door open, and waved away the smoke,
Coughed a little and started to croak,
'Are you OK?'
Questioned the man.
The waffle stood up, brushed himself off, and said, 'Call me Dan.'

He sang his little song without a care or a damn
After all there is only one waffle man.

Dan, Dan, the waffle man, faster than you think I am.
If you think you're going to eat me, think again!
Waffles on a plate, isn't my game.
Living it large, keeping it real, Birds Eye can't have THIS here meal!

He then dashed away, into the woods; and I thought he was such
                                        a cool dude.
Haven't seen him to this day, last I heard he was on a plane.
Went to somewhere not very hot.
Where he knows he isn't going to rot.

Well, that's the story of Dan, the processed potato that never
says he can't.
Take a page from his book, it might help,
God knows, I never knew that's how he felt.

Gerarld McGinnigle (15)
Deans Community High School

LITTLE SISTERS

Little sisters, they drive you mad
Even though they're the friend you never had.
Little sisters, oh they are such a pain
Sometimes they even drive you insane.

Little sisters, they drive you up the wall
You get in trouble for having a brawl.
They always start it, but you get the blame
Oh why is it always, always the same?

Little sisters , why do they exist?
Why can't they just become a myth?
All your stuff they come and take
And a mess of your room, they will make.

Little sisters, how deviously they think
I really wish I could wash them down the sink!
If I got rid of them, how happy I would be
Until I got a brother, but how annoying can they be?

Amanda McAdam (13)
Deans Community High School

SEASONS

Autumn

Colder, longer nights
When bronzen leaves
Fall from trees.

Spring

Warmer, shorter nights
When green leaves
Take their place.

Summer

Relentless sun
Toasts tiring leaves
In a struggle to survive.

Winter

Cold winter morning
Snow falls from
Laden branches.

Helen Gilbert (13)
Deans Community High School

WATER POEM

The water in the pond
is dark and deep
reflections are there to seek.
The leaves on the trees are
shimmering with the breeze.

The pillars from the sky
are the school building
nearby.
Belly-up birds dash down
into the pond, as children
come to feed them, by throwing
bread in the sky.
The shaken water ripples
in the sun, as dogs run by
barking on their backs.

Craig Henry (13)
Deans Community High School

HAUNTED HOUSE

There's a house at the top of the hill
No one lives there
Since the last family

That went missing.
I went up to the house, no friends, just me.
I touched the handle. It was cold.
I walked in. It was deserted. Dust was everywhere.
It was dark, eerie and creepy.

I heard voices, chains clanking
I walked through to a room,
I think it was the living room,
I saw a skeleton with no skull.
I kicked something. It was the skull.

Moving curtains made me shudder.
Ancient creaking stairs.
I climbed the old stairs.
Nearly every stair creaked apart from one.
The last one, the thirteenth one, the unlucky one.
Muffled screams and distant moans,
Frightening shadows on the walls.

Unoccupied bedrooms,
Dark windows, unwashed curtains,
Bloodstains on the carpet,
Gruesome bloodstains splattered on the walls.

Seems death has been here,
Aaaaaaagh!

Kimberley Allan (13)
Deans Community High School

HAUNTED

I'm running and running,
through the thick, thick forests,
I'm scared and I'm trembling like never before.
Haunted by the awful thoughts racing
                    through my head.

Going through, fast as I can,
Help! Help me please!
Over the hills and through the river,
Super-fast like Superman!
Till I'm there I won't be safe.

Still I'm running on and on,
Thick branches tug at my shoulders
Like hands that say 'Come with us.'
Terrified and trembling,
Eerie spaces, deep dark woods,
I wonder when I'll get there,
Will it be soon?

Through and through,
Running on and on
Every tree looks the same,
Might be going nowhere
But I still go on, with no
Light but the moon
Is this the end?
Never-ending journey,
Going, getting there!

Am I there yet?
Hello! Hello!
Anyone there?
No. I am all alone.

Why? Why? Why am I here?
I must keep on going,
At last, I see it.
I see my target,
Like an arrow from the bow . . .
I pounce!
Home from school at last!

Lisa Warren (13)
Deans Community High School

HAUNTED

Driving in the car,
Let's take a look.
'This big old house,
Gives me the spooks!'

Drive up the drive,
Go through the door.
We'll explore this house,
Floor by floor.

As the door opens,
There is a creak,
'Shh! What was that?
Nobody speak!'

We walk through the darkness
Into a deserted hall
Where shining suits of armour,
Stand proud and tall.

Then out of the shadows,
Comes a blood-curdling groan
I start to shiver
And wish I was home.

It's a gigantic monster
Gruesome and mean,
With clay-grey skin,
And hair that is green.

Without even thinking,
We scatter and run.
The others think this is scary
But I think this is fun.

The monster walks past us,
We sneak through the door.
I don't think I like,
This house anymore.

We jump in the car
As it starts to rain,
I don't think that we'll
Be back here again!

Lauren Jackson (13)
Deans Community High School

VIOLENCE

It eats away at flesh and bone, it snaps up every one.
It can't be stopped no matter what, it stops only when done.

Its fangs sink in and never let go, it holds until you break.
You feel the pain, the terror it brings, your life this monster takes.

And this hateful creature lurks below your bed in total silence.
This monster is after you tonight. This monster's name is Violence.

Colin G Nimmo (15)
Deans Community High School

DEATH

Death is all around us,
It has no height or weight, but it is always to be feared.
Its plans cannot be stopped, it just lurks in the darkest
corner it can find, ready to pounce.
Death fears nothing, it can never be killed.
It will be there, always ready to strike its victim.
Death chooses to move slowly or quickly and will deliver
its might blow to the unwary without conscience.

Ryan MacPherson (14)
Deans Community High School

DEATH

This is Death, it cannot be held in captivity, as it is invisible, scentless, soundless and tasteless. It cannot be touched but it can touch you.

It is everywhere; in fact at this time it is watching you and everyone around you. It watches you when you go out with your friends, when you get in the car, while you are in your home, even when you are sleeping.

It listens to you breathe and it listens to your heart as it beats against your chest. It pounces mercilessly as the body of its victim is at its weakest. It grabs hold of the body and draws the life from it. Then the victim's soul is devoured as it frantically tries to escape Death's clutches, and it is only a matter of time before it decides to take you. It will take you and everything else living, sooner or later, as it always has and always will, get its victim.

It fears nothing, and cannot be prevented. Death is the most vicious, remorseless, lethal predator this universe will ever know of, and it will be killing forever.

Robert Rae (15)
Deans Community High School

HAUNTED

The uncontrollable force keeps me from sleeping at night.
The reverberating screams pierce through my mind.
I try to escape the tortured souls but they cannot forgive.
They want revenge for my atrocity that stripped them of their lives.
My room is a glacier due to their presence,
The coldness is my heart for what I did to them.
I can see the plane, see the smoking first tower in my mind.
I can hear the pleas and the sound of screaming babies.
I can smell the sense of fear and hatred as I replay the events
                                        in my mind.
As the plane approaches its target, a bear drops from a child's arms.
I fall with it, destined for death.

Callum Gillespie (13)
Deans Community High School

SMOKING IS TOTALLY UNCOOL!

People say you have to smoke to be cool,
But really if you smoke, you are a fool.
Inside your lungs the tar gets filled,
What's the point of smoking? You just get killed!
No one who smokes has ever stopped to think,
Smoking rots your teeth and makes you stink.
Smoking cigarettes pollutes the air,
People think it's fun and do it for a dare.
All the facts mentioned in the poem are totally true,
So don't smoke, make your decision,
        It's up to you!

Jade Smith (12)
Deans Community High School

WE ARE THE SAME ON THE INSIDE

My skin colour is different,
you think I'm from the zoo,
our feet are the same,
we both have two.
My hair is curly
and it is tight,
your hair is different
because it is bright,
I have been called
some cruel names in my life,
and when it happens
it feels like being stabbed with a knife.
I have been chased into buses and a car,
but even though I keep on running
I don't get very far,
Now we have sorted it
and we are friends,
no one calls me names anymore
I hope it never ends.

Darren Macdonald (12)
Deans Community High School

NAMES

Don't they know my name is not Spoff?
They start to laugh, I turn around and know it's a cough.

They slag me off when I get it right,
Since when is it bad to be bright?

It gets worse when I get it wrong,
They make a nasty new chant or song.

Their homework is not in on time,
Mine is, is that a crime?

I want it to stop,
But they won't let it drop.

I'm in class and on time,
Oh no, I think to myself as they start another rhyme.

They all think it's a game,
Who will be first to drive me insane?

They keep it up behind my back,
Why can't they just cut me some slack?

Oh why can't they like me for who I am?

Kim Cockburn (13)
Deans Community High School

WIND. ROAD. ME.

Wind. Road. Me.
Lazy shadows of trees melting behind.
Silence except my breath,
And the persistent rhythm of my feet.

Thump, thump, thump, gasp.
Thump, thump, thump, gasp.

A submissive cat diffuses into a wall;
Its grey with the walls grey.
This body pounds on.
Alone. Powerful.

Thump, thump, gasp.

Steadily I consume the ground.
It stares after me;
A remorseless, concrete stare.
The vacant stare of a paralysed road.

Thump, gasp.
Thump, gasp.

The air grows thick and heavy now.
Inky night stains blossom darkly.
I stop.
Turn, look behind.
Observe for one second the world suspended.

Then I leave it,
Dimming into shadows above the defeated road.

Ashley Foggitt (14)
Dunbar Grammar School

HAPPINESS

Happiness is a beautiful lilac colour
Happiness tastes of sweet candy
Happiness is the smell of fresh cakes
Happiness sounds like kids having fun in the park
Happiness looks like people smiling
Happiness feels like crisp bank notes.

Charlene Collins (12)
Dunbar Grammar School

DEPRESSION

Depression is deep purple
It tastes like blood
It smells like a swamp
It looks like a dead body
It sounds like firing guns
It feels like a hammer hitting you.

Matthew Coner (11)
Dunbar Grammar School

THE DOLPHIN

A dolphin is blue
It is the winter
Under the sea
It is the colourful rainbow
It is a leather jacket
It is a leather couch
It is a flipper
Boiled liver.

David Ritchie (12)
Dunbar Grammar School

HAPPINESS

Happiness is rosy pink,
It tastes like candyfloss
melting in your mouth,
It smells like blossom in
the trees,
It looks like a snowy Christmas,
It sounds like someone laughing,
Happiness is the excitement
in your heart.

Alanah McGovern (12)
Dunbar Grammar School

HAPPINESS

Happiness is a bright yellow,
It tastes like candyfloss melting,
It smells like blossom in the trees,
It looks like a snowy Christmas,
It sounds like children laughing,
Happiness is lying on the beach.

Laura McNeill (11)
Dunbar Grammar School

WITCH

A witch is green.
She is the wintertime,
in her dark cottage,
it is stormy,
She wears a long, leather, black
and green jacket.
She is a large broomstick,
She is a Blair Witch project,
A spicy hot potion which is poisonous.

Sobea Ahmed (12)
Dunbar Grammar School

HAPPINESS

Happiness is a bright red,
It tastes like fresh strawberries,
It smells like a red rose,
It looks like a newborn baby,
It sounds like chiming bells,
Happiness feels like a soft blanket.

Victoria Brown (12)
Dunbar Grammar School

JOY

Joy is a warm orange,
It tastes like a chocolate river,
It smells like fresh baking,
It looks like a smile,
Joy sounds like laughter,
Joy feels like I'm sleeping in my bed.

Vicky Bertaut (11)
Dunbar Grammar School

WITCH

The witch is a freaky black,
She is a freezing cold autumn,
A witch is the dark streets of Edinburgh,
She is thunder and lightning weather,
A big, black, pointed hat, a long, tall stool,
She is Hocus Pocus. A big, black pudding.

Claire Millar (12)
Dunbar Grammar School

HATE

Hate is a bitter red,
It tastes like sour milk,
It smells of Brussels sprouts,
It looks like someone being brutally tortured,
It sounds like pins dropping on a hard floor.
Hate is as solid as a rock!

Callum Miller (11)
Dunbar Grammar School

ANGER!

Anger is dark red.
It tastes like a hot vindaloo.
It smells like fire.
It looks like a burning building.
It sounds like a runaway freight train.
Anger is as hot as a steaming kettle.

Kevin Addies (12)
Dunbar Grammar School

ANGER

Anger is dark, dark red,
It tastes like rotten potatoes,
It smells like a burning forest,
It looks like war with guns firing everywhere,
It sounds like people howling in the distance,
Anger is as hot as a burning fire.

Jonathan Hendrie (12)
Dunbar Grammar School

WITCH

A witch is black,
She is the autumn time
In a basement,
She is stormy,
A witch is a big, black hat,
A big, fat cauldron
A bowl of frogs' legs.

Haylie Stewart (11)
Dunbar Grammar School

LOVE

Love is a rosy red
It tastes like sweet strawberries
It smells like rose petals
It looks like an orchard of butterflies
It sounds like birds in the morning
Love feels like a . . .
. . . cuddle

Síobhan Malone (12)
Dunbar Grammar School

HAPPINESS

Happiness is bright orange,
It tastes like fresh fish,
It smells like a new house,
It looks like a newborn puppy,
It sounds like birds whistling
                    in the morning,
It feels like a big, bright star!

Kerry Hyland (12)
Dunbar Grammar School

OCTOPOEM - FOOTBALLER

A footballer is bright yellow
He is summertime
On a pitch,
He is yellow sunshine,
A clean white strip,
A tall wide trophy cabinet,
A match of the day,
Oranges at half-time.

William Arthur (12)
Dunbar Grammar School

INSPIRATION, SAFE FROM THE FLAMES

It all began with a single cow,
But who knows where it will end?
A hundred thousand million animals,
All could end up dead.

Hundreds and thousands of farms affected.
More and more cases each day.
So many animals killed, slaughtered.
Is there no easier way?

There's no stopping this silent killer,
As the air becomes thick with a fog.
The souls of all the animals that've died,
Are encased in a thick black smog.

But out of the ash cloud,
Comes a glimmer of hope,
Her mother stands over her,
Proud.
The ruby-red fur of this calf, still wet,
Her eyes glitter like a jewel in a crown.

Her long black lashes,
And bold brown eyes.
I admire her there,
As she still lies.
She's untouched, innocent,
Pure as snow,
But will she ever really know,
Just how much inspiration she has been?
Guardian angel,
Helping me forget what I've seen.

No smoke, no fire.
No funeral pyre.
Just birth.
Not death.
Tears of joy.

This shimmering angel.
A symbol.
For she inspires us all
We must keep fighting
To the end.
Our farm will never fall.

Angela Peters (16)
Dunbar Grammar School

DARK FEAR

Fear is fiery red,
It tastes like frozen maggots,
It smells like rotten bodies,
It looks like Hell burning away,
It sounds like a teacher shouting at you,
Fear feels like a sword going through you.

Stefan Diamond (12)
Dunbar Grammar School

COLD RAGE

The Coldness of a Supernova burning deep within my breast,
The apathetic rage of cool and collected fury,
The strength and determination of anger can be utilised,
The Cold Rage,
Speak now or forever hold your peace.

The winding melodies seek to break through the self-induced isolation,
Take a step back, then another,
Always to be announced, never emotions now,
The Cold Rage.
Remember this moment.

Trapped inside these musing verses are the shards of emotions,
Cooled too quick, now brittle and shattered.
Remember this moment.
Beyond pain.

The rage and turmoil of a last chance,
The bitter and lonely petals of a black rose,
The thorns cut too deep,
Too close to the heart.
The Cold Rage.

When the pressure of all feelings push in from all sides,
The bubble of solitude holds,
Renewed from second to second.

Indefinable,
The Cold Rage,
Never forget this moment.
Always renew the bubble,
Yield and the bubble bursts.

Gabriel Brady (13)
George Heriot's School

AT THE END

Why is life so hard?
Will we ever get our reward?
When we finally come to the end,
Will there be a path at the dead end?

Will we again meet a best friend?
Will we get a chance for a better end?
Will we all have to face our fears?
And will this strength come so near,
 to reaching everlasting rest,
  inside our own eternal nest?

Euan Reid (11)
George Heriot's School

ZIGZAG WORLD

In the Zigzag World
Everything, as you can
probably guess
Is zigzag
Quite frankly, it looks like a mess.

The frogs have zigs
And the toads have zags
The cows hate pigs
And the giraffes wear bags.

Humans in the Zigzag World
are blue and purple
And sometimes burble.
The most important thing
About the Zigzag World
is . . .

It's totally insane!

Susan Wilson (11)
George Heriot's School

TRAINING

The first day of call-up
When we climbed out of the truck
The Sergeant Major yelled at us
For falling in the muck.

The officers had their mess
Their rooms, they were the best
But our dirty down-trodden barracks
Really had much less.

Gym was a disaster
They told us to run faster
Charlie hit the wall bars
Now his arm's in plaster.

Ropes weren't much better
Ally lost his sweater
Harry fell in the water
And now we're even wetter.

Rifles weren't much fun
I shot a drainpipe with my gun
So the Sergeant Major said -
'You can't hit a barn door
Let alone the Hun!'

On the final day's parade
The Sergeant gave us a marching aid.
But even with this handy guide,
Oh what a mess we made!

Dick marched like a bear
Tom said it was a dare
Oh well I'm home now
Training, what a nightmare!

Robbie Lyon (12)
George Heriot's School

CHRISTMAS EVE

Christmas Eve sparkles with joy,
It's the day before I get a brand new toy!

The clock stands in the hall, ticking by,
Waiting for Santa to arrive.

The fairy sits at the top of the tree,
Watching over everyone, including me!

A group of robins chatter in the backyard,
I think they're all Santa's guards!

The stockings hang by the chimney like pheasants,
Shouting at Santa to fill them with presents!!

Nicola Shand (12)
George Heriot's School

HEAVEN

I'm out of this world
On a silent beach
No one can touch me,
I'm out of reach.

With the wind in my hair
And the sand in my toes
No one can touch me,
And nobody knows.

Where the sky is like water
And the birds are like fish,
No one can touch me
No matter how hard they wish.

The sun is dying down
I'll make a wish,
No one can touch me
Let me stay in this bliss.

Eilidh Gillanders (11)
George Heriot's School

THE FIRE

It lit up the dull, black night
Leaping orange flames,
Slowly licking, dancing, calling
Playing its deadly games.
I watched it from my window
Kneeling on my bed,
I heard the dreadful cries
I smelt the burning lead.

The fire leapt from house to house
Eating up lives, giving out pain,
Their bodies quickly cooking
It wasn't long till our turn came.
Through my open window, many a spark flew
My curtains started to blaze,
The bed covers caught alight
Yet still I sat in a daze.

The room suddenly sparked with life
I panicked and turned to flee,
But to my dismay was trapped
A scorching, evil demon surrounded me.
The room was enveloped in a thick, black smoke
The toxic fumes were strong,
They stuck to my throat making me splutter
This was Hell, I wouldn't last long.

I fell to the ground,
Where I was drowned,
By the scorching black demon
                    of fire!

Jenny Trendell (11)
George Heriot's School

THE HORSE

Horses, bold and beautiful
A loyal friend to have.
Their power overwhelming.
An ever-loving beast of glory.

Horses, fast and furious
As they canter, trot and gallop.
And features which are of desire,
Are their long legs which never seem to tire.

Horses, grand and gracious.
With that irresistible charm.
That special touch that makes you smile
And makes you love them even more.

Horses, sturdy and steady
A survivor to the end
Standing brave and fearless
Never one to pretend.

Horses, precise and precious
The most gentle beast alive
Who could hate their loving eyes
Which have a way to hypnotise?

Horses, calm and careful
As they venture through a wood
Who could not, but adore
Their great willingness for more?

Ealasaid Manson (12)
George Heriot's School

THE BEST THING ABOUT THE BEACH

The golden, tingling sand,
Beneath my carefree feet,
The soothing dark blue ripples,
Of the sparkling sea seat.

I'd never want to imagine,
To look up and never see,
The never-ending horizon line,
That has always comforted me.

The swishing cool air,
That hits my face with delight,
The warm bright sun,
That makes me feel so bright.

But the best thing of all,
However brilliant the view can be,
Is being with my family,
Treading together, along the fascinating beach.

Amani Khader (12)
George Heriot's School

WATER

Refreshing the senses, refreshing the mind,
Water is so bracing, it's one of a kind.
It comes in many shapes and forms,
Rivers, lakes, showers, storms.

It is so important, no one can deny,
Water is vital, without it, we'd die.
It supplies us with verve, it supplies us with life,
It renews our spirits through struggle and strife.

Water isn't always as safe as it seems,
Occasionally great floods pour from its streams,
Tsunamis and tidal waves cause devastation,
It's Mother Nature's punishment for destroying her nation.

Fortunately, water is usually serene,
Supporting all life, land and marine.
We must hope that it stays the same,
Gentle, peaceful, calm and tame.

Kathryn Alexander (11)
George Heriot's School

WHEN I WRITE A POEM.

Everybody says that 'Poems are hard to write,
When you sit and brainstorm, your thoughts fly out of sight!'
But when I'm feeling ready and my pencil's in my hand,
I can write quite efficiently and rhyme so very grand.

When my head starts churning and my pencil starts to race
My thoughts flow like rivers and my heart beats over-pace
I can run so quick through poems - fast as fast can be
I never get a chance to stop - my brain is in top gear.

But when I hear that bell ring, my pencil starts to drop
My head gives up its churning and my rhyming starts to stop.
I feel like jumping from my seat and yelling in despair;
'Come on, just five more minutes!' but I know that isn't fair.

Anna Lazarski (12)
George Heriot's School

A USE FOR GRANNIES

The press just want to make it clear,
That the hole in the ozone layer is causing fear,
Therefore, I shall fix this very large hole,
With a bit of logic right from my soul.

Now if you kindly would recall,
What your granny is like, short or tall,
It doesn't matter whether she is clever or mad,
As long as she's a granny and not a dad.

Secondly, she needs to be good at complaining,
About money and jobs or the fact that it's raining,
Thirdly, she needs to be able to knit,
Otherwise she'll have a job keeping fit.

All these grannies will meet at two,
To board the balloon and go off into the blue,
Where they will rise to the ozone layer,
Where they can't complain about pensions or the mayor.

So up they go in their balloon,
And knit their pants off by the light of the moon,
So the rest of their life they enjoy up there,
Keeping fit until they knit without a care.

So there is the government's problem solved,
And in case you were wondering the ozone layer has evolved,
Because now there is not a hole in sight,
But a very neat woolly cover keeping the hole shut tight!

Rebecca Harris-Evans (12)
George Heriot's School

MORNING JOURNEY

Off to school (again).
Did not want to go.
Dreaded what I had that day:
PE, music, maths, history,
RME, English, double biology.

Morning journey - very long, and tiring.
Fitted in some last minute revision
(In case I got something wrong.)

Transport going slower.
Didn't want to be late,
But wouldn't mind missing assembly.

Off the bus, turn the corner,
And on up the path.
Knew I was late - everyone had gone inside.
Through old, small black gate.
Across the playground, past the door,
trying not to trip over bags on the floor.
Along the corridor, into class.
Heave a sigh, there at last.

Calum Jones (12)
George Heriot's School

NOISES

The murmur of voices from the lounge,
The groaning of my dog,
The droning of the television,
The insistent ticking of a clock.
A moth fluttering at the light bulb,
A gurgling in the pipes,
A clatter of dishes in the kitchen,
And the rain spattering on my window.
The roof tiles doing a Mexican wave,
The wind whistling under the front door,
The urgent screech of brakes on the road,
The dripping of a tap.
A bus hissing as it stops outside,
A dog's distant bay.
Creaking of floorboards coming closer!
Then gently ebbing away.
Noises I hear snuggled up in my bed,
Some scary, yet comforting.
    Then peace.

Ross Collinson (12)
George Heriot's School

THE BEGINNING

Trapped,
Suffocating,
Struggling,
Squirming,

Pushing to freedom,
Forcing through to air,
Intake of breath,
Freedom at last.

Crying, wailing,
Blinding lights,
Tossing around,
Dunking in water.

Warmth and comfort,
Relaxed, at ease,
Loving arms,
Beautiful face.

Kindly smile,
Glinting eyes,
Softest lips,
Gentle voice.

The perfect mother
To whom I was born.

Charles Ibbett (12)
George Heriot's School

THE SEAGULL

Sammy the starving seagull,
Was searching for a snack.
He saw a scrumptious salmon,
And swooped down to attack.

Sammy scoffed the salmon,
As swiftly as a snake,
But that was barely starters,
'I now feel like some hake!'

Stuffed and slightly sleepy,
Sammy soared into the sky,
When suddenly he saw the sun,
And cried out 'I'm too high!'

Sammy screeched and shouted,
But he was just too late,
He hit the sun and sizzled,
Like a sausage on a plate.

He looked down at his feathers,
And saw that they were singed,
'Oh no, they are all ruined!'
Sammy sadly whinged.

He spiralled down towards the sea,
And called out in distress,
He struck the water with such speed,
That his body went to rest.

But Sammy's spirit still survived,
Even after the disaster,
And it went to seagull Heaven,
To live happily ever after.

Chris Wickes (12)
George Heriot's School

THE CAMEL

Camel, camel burning bright,
In the deserts of the night
No other sturdy hoof or eye
Could frame thy great hump's symmetry.

In what distant pack of lies,
Are nomads telling of the size,
Of this great creature's strong desire,
Never to stop even if it's on fire.

From far they came to the camel's part,
To watch him never give up heart,
And then the camel heard the beat,
Of tens of thousands of sandalled feet.

'Twould have to be a powerful chain,
To lead him to this awful pain,
Even if it could not grasp,
The wonderful life it used to clasp.

When the crowd began to jeer,
The poor old camel shed a tear,
He could not understand or see,
Why he wasn't allowed to turn and flee.

Camel, camel, burning bright,
In the deserts of the night,
That evil crowd brought by a lie
Have framed his great hump's symmetry.

Stuart Cullen (12)
George Heriot's School

POETRY SHOULD BE FUN

Pen poised, but nothing comes.
Inspiration? There is none.
Is it this hard for everyone?
Writing poetry should be fun.

I'm focused, but still devoid of an idea.
The empty page a growing fear
As the homework deadline is looming near
I'm sure this assignment will end in tears.

I know I can do this, I've done it before
But somehow this time it seems such a chore
My rejected ideas collect on the floor
As the frustration inside me grows more and more.

Hours drag by, first one, then two,
But still no progress, no breakthrough
I remain uncertain what to do
Only circling thoughts, nothing new.

No more time for procrastination,
Or I'll never be the poet of the nation
And with great determination
I vow to resolve this situation.

Suddenly an idea comes to mind.
Why didn't I think of it before?
Poetry doesn't need to rhyme,
It should be fun and not a bore!

Aja Murray (11)
George Heriot's School

THE HOCKEY MATCH

Putting on our hockey kit and tying back our hair,
Fiddling with our hockey sticks as we prepare.
Sitting in the changing room, everyone's ready now
Waiting to get on the pitch, furrowing the brow.

Standing in position with our sticks to the ground,
Looking in the eyes of the opposition, my heart begins to pound.
Waiting for the whistle, tension in the air,
As I stand fixed to the spot, I say a silent prayer.

The whistle blows, I dive straight for the ball,
I dribble up the field 'Score, score!' they call.
Just when I think I'm about to succeed,
The defender tackles. What a tackle indeed!

I'm tired of running, all puffed out,
'Come on, keep going!' Our coach begins to shout.
With a new surge of confidence, I fly up the pitch,
Dodge past the defender, past any hitch.

I'm soaring now, without a thought;
Not for the people around me - the team I've got.
I strike the ball and it's going to go in,
The goalie misses, oh what a win!

Sarah G Lyall (11)
George Heriot's School

MY CAT

Proudly she prowls with her sleek black fur,
it feels like silk as it runs through my fingers
she starts to purr.

Queen of all she surveys, with her x-ray stare,
seeing all, knowing all, there are no secrets from
her regal glare.

She lies in her basket, sleeping snug, warm, tight
she darts quickly, hardly visible, hunting
through the night.

The pinpricks like stars that are her eyes, spot the prey.
The stare fixes, the whiskers twitch, she grins.
She knows she'll get her way.

Then, when she returns to the warmth of the house,
she curls up on my lap. Safe in happy dreams,
she catches a mouse.

I love her dearly, she knows that.
My proud, sleek, regal, cuddly cat.

Natasha Donald (11)
George Heriot's School

MUSIC

'And what are your hobbies?' They all then ask me,
'Books, games, swimming, or maybe all three?'
I have lots of pastimes at all times of the year,
But my favourite is my music, as you will soon hear.

When very small I heard 'The Four Seasons'
Often on my way to school.
Clever Vivaldi - spring, summer, autumn, winter
All flowed together with a melodic tool.

At six I started the piano,
And well known tunes then filled our house.
I love to play loudly with gusto,
Or sometimes as quietly as a mouse.

And later, I started the recorder.
What fun I had at Tuesday lunch -
Solos, sonnets and carols in Greyfriars
We were a very cheery bunch!

My flute is my newest musical challenge,
Slim, silver, light and pure
My summer course called Tutti Flutey
Helped me a great deal, that's for sure.

In this endless array of a fascinating art,
It would be difficult to know where to start,
Life would be dull with no music to hear,
I look forward to more, year after year.

Emily Frier (11)
George Heriot's School

THE CHIP SHOP

T he chip shop is my favourite place
H addock and chips, brought from the ships
E veryone standing in a queue

C hips and brown sauce, just for you
H appy faces everywhere
I nto their faces go the chips
P ies greasy, peas mushy, it's not enough

S moked sausage suppers sizzling
H aggis battered by the crew
O ld and young enjoy it too
P uffed and bloated, away we go.
   Oh my God, I'm about to blow!

Jed Case (11)
George Heriot's School

THE COCKLE TRAIN, PORT ELLIOT - GOOLWA, AUSTRALIA

C risp sound
O ne o'clock each day
C hildren wave as it fires past
K illing rubbish as it speeds along
L iving still, from 75 years ago
E cstatic children suffer to go on this masterpiece

T he wind is baking, whipping, and a knife in your face
R ipping apart tracks, as it gatecrashes on its tour
A ustralia, Goolwa to Port Elliot
I ndian ocean is within our sight on the tour
N orth wind whips your face

Douglas Holligan (12)
George Heriot's School

DREAMS

As bedtime comes around at last,
I wonder what magical place I shall visit tonight.
For in my dreams anything could happen,
I only have to close my eyes.

Tonight, I visit a place of peace,
Where there is no war or crime.
The air is filled with love and care,
And there is happiness all around.

Warm, bright colours surround me,
Laughter is all I hear.
A small taste of Heaven,
There is no room in this place for fear.

Everyone here is treated the same,
Everything here is fair.
There are no poor with nowhere to go,
There's no force anywhere.

This is such a lovely place,
Where everyone is friendly and kind.
I would love to visit a place like that,
If only it wasn't a dream.

Kirsty Bell (11)
George Heriot's School

A STEAM RAILWAY

I love to go to steam railways
I love the smell of the coal
The oily, tarry smell of the engine
Waiting to haul our train away

I love the look of the engine
The glossy paint and immaculate brass
The greasy driver mops his brow
As the fireman tends the swirling fire

I love the engine's shrill whistle
I love the banging of the doors
The chuffing and puffing and hiss of steam
As the engine strains under its heavy load

I love the taste of fishpaste sandwiches
Washed down with a warm cup of tea
As the conductor slides open the compartment door
With a cry of 'Tickets please'

I love the feel of first class upholstery
The luxury feel of travelling in style
The sense of adventure when out in the world
And the comfort of coming back home.

Jonathan Hodges (11)
George Heriot's School

A WALK IN THE GRAVEYARD

My footsteps were light,
So light, oh so light,
Weaving through the dead.

A blood-chilling howl
Ripped through the air,
My blood was ice
Crawling in my veins,
Slowly. Slowly.

The moon tore from behind the clouds,
Shining with all its glory.
Bathing me in its eerie light
Over the graves and distant hills.
Dark magic was working,
Everything was mysterious and terrifying,
Yet strangely calm.
I watched, scared but soothed,
I didn't want the spell to be broken,
I was entranced
By the beauty of it all.

But nothing wonderful ever lasts,
The graves creaked and groaned,
The dead were rising,
I felt a scream dying on my lips.

Jerkily they sat up,
I sat watching, silently,
I was an intruder
They made me one of them.

I became a creature of the night
But beware, for I shall be preying on you!

Zeby Kwok (12)
George Heriot's School

SCOTLAND

The fresh air we inhale
The countryside we admire
The rainy weather we so often see
Is all part of mighty Scotland

The high-spirited sheep on the hills in the distance
The cattle eating to their hearts content, in the fields
The salmon leaping in the relaxing calm locks
Is all part of mighty Scotland

The fresh, crisp whisky
The traditional haggis
The tremendous tatties
Is all part of mighty Scotland

The best place in the world to be
The inspirational countryside
The delicious typical food
Is the one and only mighty Scotland.

Ruth Ostrowski (11)
George Heriot's School

MY SANCTUARY

I come in after a day of school
Kick my shoes off
Flop down on my bed.

The feel of the smooth, soft duvet
The sight of my sky-blue walls,
It's all so soothing.
I feel so free,
Like a bird soaring through the sky.

I can listen to my thoughts,
No interruptions.
Just my thoughts and I
Away from the rest of the world.

I'm so calm
I'm so happy,
Just to be in my special place
My bedroom
My sanctuary.

Kemi Oyeneyin (12)
George Heriot's School

THE HILL

One fine spring morning, I climbed a bonny hill,
I climbed and I climbed until my feet were sore.
I waited and waited until everything was still,
Then I got a view like a hawk, as if
I was in the sky which they ruled.

The heather whistled in the breeze,
As I splashed my way through a burn of crystal.
My legs were bristled by the leaves of the thistle,
One fine spring morning, I climbed a bonny hill.

Alex Crawford (11)
George Heriot's School

THE WORLD

The world is a funny place,
Fully surrounded by space.

The world is very tall,
And round, like a bouncy ball.

The world moans and the world groans,
And the people of Earth, have cellular phones.

Chris Steuart (11)
George Heriot's School

A PLACE I KNOW
MY MAGICAL HOUSE

When you come inside my house
You see lots of different things
Things you might not see in yours
Like pigs that fly with wings!

When you come inside my house
You see lots of strange stuff
Stuff you might not see in yours
Like dragons that breathe, puff puff!

When you come inside my house
You see lots of weird folk
Folk you might not see in yours
Like frogs jumping around, croak, croak!

When you come inside my house
You come into my hall
A hall a little different from yours
With monkeys havin' a ball!

When you come inside my house
You come to my bedroom
A bedroom a bit different from yours
With a Grand Prix track, broom broom!

When you come inside my house
You come to my living room
A living room a little different from yours
With wild cheetahs zoom zoom!

My house may sound strange to you
But please, don't worry
Just because it sounds a little odd
I would like you to come back in a hurry!

Sean Lowson (12)
George Heriot's School

AMERICAN STATES

I lived in America, the golden states
There are many places I like and places I hate
They're all different in one way or another
I know loads of states from the north to the south
I lived in Ohio, the flattest, with fields and plains
Michigan was fun, to start the skiing games
Colorado was when skiing became real, when I went to Vail
Arizona with cactuses and hearing a cowboy's tale
Utah was spectacular with red rocks and blue lakes
California was a variety, with its famous bridge - Golden Gate
Montana, where you rode a horse to meet with a grizzly bear
Illinois with Chicago, climbing skyscrapers, if you dare
There are many, many more, as I'm sure you know
America is the place that I just love to go.

Victoria Clark (12)
George Heriot's School

ALONE WITH THE BEACH

Alone, no one's there, just you and the beach
The raft floats in the clear blue water
You sit on it, watching the boats in the bay
A family comes down the stairs from the woods.
Three small children playing merrily in the sand,
Trying to build a car or boat, you cannot tell.
They eat, pack up and leave.
Evening comes, you're still there
Silence falls again, alone on the beach.
The onlooker on the raft smiles and draws
A crumpled photo out of his pocket
Of his family, far away.

Margot Clair Rayner (11)
George Heriot's School

GOLDEN ACRE

G olden Acre is a place of sport
O f happiness, fun and joy,
L ots of cheers, noises of all sorts
D etermination in every girl and boy
E very player has good games
N obody has anything bad.

A lways playing different teams
C heering me on is my dad.
R ugby, hockey, tennis and more
E vermore played on Golden Acre's grassy floor.

Calum Humphries (11)
George Heriot's School

LOCH NESS

Rippling waves splashing the pebbly shore,
Boats swaying on the untouched surface of the water.
Small freshwater streams slithering down the majestic rolling hillside.
A golden eagle soars overhead and dips its ravenous beak
Into the pearly water and glides away into the setting sun
With a fish struggling in its grasp.
The sun sets, casting an eerie shadow over Loch Ness.

Steven Smith (12)
George Heriot's School

THE HAUNTED HOUSE

The old black house sits high on the hill
Its rooftop reaching the sky.
The house is deserted and no one there
But is lively as a fairground at night.

The house has shrieks and shadowy figures
That are there for only a second.
You get a pat on the shoulder and chills in the air
You look behind and no one is there.

You never feel alone in that house I bet
But no one around could witness it.
No one I know can tell their fate
Because alas, you don't come out alive.

The house is owned by souls alone
And devils of years gone by,
Maybe one day I'll enter that house
But maybe that day I'll *die!*

Jenny McIntyre (12)
George Heriot's School

PANTHER

He needs:
Sleek midnight fur
A soft glowing purr
Claws that click on the ground
A tail that swishes without sound.
Bright autumn eyes
Teeth as sharp as a thousand knives.
A mouth like a never-ending cave,
He needs to be bold and brave,
With gracefulness and poise,
He prowls without noise.

Rebecca Carnie (12)
George Heriot's School

AN ANGEL FLOATING SKYWARDS

She lay as fragile sunflowers touched her golden hair,
She lay all alone, yet she was not the only one there.
The breeze spoke softly, with caring, calm intent,
She didn't hear a word, but knew exactly what it meant.
The corn around her swayed in the wind, that didn't blow.
It sang the song she'd never heard, yet every word did know.
The sun beat down upon her skin, so soft as she lay there
The world and her were one again, she was drained of every care,
She lay back on the golden ground and looked up at the sky.
She watched the clouds form whirlpools and more back did she lie,
And then a finch did chirp and started to sing along.
To the natural orchestra, which played the soothing song.
A smile dances across her face, she lay back further still,
She floated down and through the ground, but not against her will.
Then with closed eyes she took a breath and was at complete peace,
And then her angel, spirit, soul, outwards did release.

Philip Shaw (13)
George Heriot's School

A JOB DESCRIPTION FOR THE OCEAN

You need:

A '1' in standard grade sand sculpture
A confident communication with coral.
A salty smacked scent that gets up your nose.
No foes.
Water that is as clear as crystal,
Animal attention award 'A'.
A colour that is purely deep blue
Fool's gold for sand too,
If you have these qualities, then this job is perfect for you.

Elspeth Cockburn (13)
George Heriot's School

PEREGRINE FALCON

He needs:

Wings like long, thin, soft downy kites
A body like a plastic bottle, long and light,
A head like an oval pom-pom, light and soft,
Eyes like marbles - strong and bright.
A beak like scissors - strong, sharp and slight,
Claws like craft knives, built for cutting and
Sharpness.
A tail like a fan spread out and light.
These features make a peregrine falcon.

James Stevenson (13)
George Heriot's School

DOLPHIN

He needs:

A body like the silvery reflection of a white candle
Fins that glide like a kite soaring in the sky on a crisp autumn day,
A flipper that moves as elegantly as the swirling snow,
The strength of a golden eagle, scooping and diving for prey, yet
A grace that is felt only by a dancer, leaping through the air.

A flash of aqua in the royal blue sea
The beauty of the tiger's leap in the still plain.
The swiftness of a single drop of water
Landing in a skydive puddle.
The energy of a firework, displaying all its glory . . .
And then, a few lifeless bubbles floating gently
On the water's surface.

Emma Stewart (13)
George Heriot's School

PERHAPS

I'm sitting here thinking how can I stop?
My head is just swimming, swimming with thoughts
I can see him tomorrow: I can see him today.
But I know he will always, be far, far away.

If only for once, I could reach out and touch.
His eyes are so dark I could lighten them up,
I would smile and laugh
And know what to say -
I pray that soon
I might come to this day.

I hear his voice,
So soft and so sad.
As it fills up inside me
The space I always had.
That empty hole is suddenly warm,
His dedication and love
So relaxing and calm.

So when he does
What he does best
It fills me up inside:
My heart is pounding,
My eyes alight -
He really is a charming sight.

I see his smile
My breath disappears
My knee starts to tremble
I feel the tears.
Every second I spare
Every moment I see
Perhaps one day he will look back at me.

Charlotte A Wells (14)
George Heriot's School

BLISSFUL ISOLATION

In the centre of a diamond sky,
Lies the world which is my own
Mortals, why can't you let me be?
In my blissful state of isolation.

You cannot understand my plea,

My need to be with my state of mind,
Warped and twisted dreams of fate,
Mix gladly in a void of darkness,
Mending shards of devastation,
Healing my now shattered soul.

My need to be with those whom I love,
With a being of utter confusion.
Yet you do not know my pain,
When you tear me from isolation.

So darkness takes my injured soul.
Takes me to a harsh cold world,
No longer in my state of bliss,
Wrenched into your reality.

Why can't you let me be?
In my blissful state of isolation.

Laura Johnstone (14)
George Heriot's School

I Saw a Fish . . .

I saw a fish spit out flame,
I saw a gun go insane.
I saw an ape eat a mouse,
I saw a cat as big as a house.
I saw a hill on a chair,
I saw a coat with long red hair.
I saw a cow, a deep dark blue,
I saw the sky eating a shoe.
I saw a dog flying up high
I saw a wren starting to cry.
I saw a child crashing on rocks,
I saw a sea pairing socks.
I saw a mum blossom in spring,
I saw a huge oak on a gold ring.
I saw a diamond go to bed,
I saw a man drop down dead.

Callum Young (13)
George Heriot's School

I SAW . . .

I saw a traffic light turn to green
I saw some grass being munched by a cow
I saw some meat being eaten by a cannibal
I saw a vegetarian consume a vegetable
I saw a piece of fruit on a branch
I saw a tree in the wild
I saw a bear wrestle with a man
I saw a ring shine of gems
I saw a ruby red as fire
I saw the hot sun blaze down on Earth
I saw the sea full of ice-cold water
I saw a glass six foot deep
I saw a ditch brimming with mud
I saw a dirty garment lying on the ground
I saw a floor swept completely clean
I saw a sponge underneath the sink
I saw a tap ejecting cold water
I saw a fountain standing tall
I saw a giant beside a midget
I saw a dwarf, who saw all of this.

Caroline Adams (12)
George Heriot's School

I SAW A STONE FLOAT THROUGH THE AIR

I saw a stone float through the air,
I saw a cloud with long flowing hair,
I saw a woman in the dead of night
I saw a star with a deadly bite.
I saw a snake with thin, webbed feet,
I saw a duck with an old rusty seat.
I saw an abandoned truck with long sharpened nails,
I saw an old hand with high, flapping sails.
I saw a boat with bright colourful petals,
I saw a flower with bars of bare metals.
I saw a depressing prison, looking for love
I saw the world with a clear, plastic glove,
I saw a caring doctor wailing out in despair
I saw the injured enjoying the scare.
I saw the evil even in the darkest of nights,
Thank goodness we can't see these sights.

Jenny Alexander (12)
George Heriot's School

POEM - I SAW THE STARS

I saw the stars dancing in the trees
I saw the birds whisper in the breeze,
I saw a kite burrowing into the ground
I saw a mole as he was crowned.
I saw the king playing the fool
I saw a clown being cool,
I saw an iceberg engulfed in flames,
I saw a furnace overcome with shame.
I saw a criminal as he sailed over a lake,
I saw a swan quiver and shake.
I saw an Eskimo pick some flowers,
I saw a child count down the hours.
I saw an astronaut swim through the sea,
I saw a dolphin just like you and me.
I saw an alien dance as if on air,
I saw a ballerina bearing a mare.
I saw a horse down on her knees,
I saw a beggar in a limousine.
I saw a star shining bright above
I saw the moon as white as a dove.
I saw the cat that got the cream,
And what's more, I saw it all in a dream.

Mark J R Scott (13)
George Heriot's School

FADING MEMORIES

I saw a cloud filled with tears alone,
I saw a living body without a single bone,
I saw a graveyard filled with joy,
I saw a weeping child with a toy,
I saw a grown man shrink in size,
I saw a fire fed purely by lies.
I saw the Devil sing a love song,
I saw an angry wolf cry out in pain,
I saw the spirit of integrity, lost in a world of the vain,
I saw the deepest heart scream and die,
I saw a baby bird teach its elder to fly.
I saw a sunflower get up and dance with style,
I saw the saddest man, usher a smile
I saw the sun after years of rain,
I saw thousands of people whose lives became plain.
I saw a family of clocks weeping for their mother's chime,
I saw the church bells ring and take us through time.
I saw the first aeroplane cascade through the sky,
I saw all of these memories wave goodbye.

Richard Bell (13)
George Heriot's School

CRASH STRAIGHT TO THE GROUND

I saw an island filled with sun
I saw the sky as clear as day
I saw a woman wearing black
I saw them weep inside the church
I saw the flowers by my side
I saw a mountain full of glossy trees
I saw my reflection in the autumn breeze
I saw a squirrel jump from tree to tree
I saw a monkey in the midst of the forest
I saw a cottage with a pond outside
I saw a swan perched on the ground
I saw a snowflake fall from above
I saw a bird crash straight to the ground

I heard a scream from the end of the lane
I heard the crack from the windowpanes
I heard the glass shatter all around
I hear the rain spit down on the ground
I heard the children laughing out loud
I heard the adults in the pub
I heard a cry as a ghost appeared
I heard a flash come from the sky
I heard the thunder crash straight to the ground.

Sophie Pia (13)
George Heriot's School

I Saw A Mountain...

I saw a mountain drop out of the sky
I saw rain starting to cry,
I saw a baby swallow an aeroplane
I saw a cloud smile in disdain.
I saw an old man swim the ocean blue,
I saw a dolphin split in two.
I saw an atom covered in lipstick,
I saw a wine glass drip blood from a rose stem prick,
I saw a finger turn life upside down,
I saw a murderer - the home of the royal crown.
I saw a palace with a river running through it,
I saw a rainforest lost without a spirit.
I saw a ghost, red-faced and dying,
I saw a blind woman see the world, crying.
I saw God as he magically drew
I saw flowers to say I love you.

Sarah Sandison (13)
George Heriot's School

THE DREAMS I HAVE SEEN

I saw a cauliflower grow a nose,
I saw Pinocchio in his lederhose.
I saw an Austrian swallow a fly,
I saw a frog fall from the sky.
I saw a star blazing hot with rage,
I saw a man bellowing words from a page.
I saw somebody read with their eyes tightly shut,
I saw someone sleep on the shell of a nut.
I saw an ant marching with a uniform on,
I saw a soldier chirping a song.
I saw a bluebird turning gold,
I saw the sun growing old.
I saw myself seeing what I had seen,
I saw again, these wonderful dreams.

Naomi Howarth (13)
George Heriot's School

I Saw A Peacock With A Fiery Tail

I saw a peacock with a fiery tail,
I saw a tiger starting to wail,
I saw a baby reading a book,
I saw a teacher learning to cook.
I saw a child playing excitedly with a ball,
I saw a cat wander casually through a hall.
I saw a minister reaching wide and far
I saw an oak holding a large metal bar.
I saw a madman with lots of eyes,
I saw a peacock with a fiery tail.

Graeme Acheson (12)
George Heriot's School

I SENSED THE OCEAN . . .

I sensed the ocean engulfed in flames,
I sensed the bonfire, freezing the people,
I sensed the fridge, cooking the food,
I sensed the loving family, isolated from each other.
I sensed the fugitives, wandering around the town,
I sensed the shoppers without any money,
I sensed the poor man as he ran his bank,
I sensed the thief as he was arrested in innocence.
I sensed the policeman, swimming casually in a pool,
I sensed the duck, chasing the cat,
I sensed the mouse who overpowered the humans,
I sensed the ghost who was frightened of the dark,
I sensed the candle, which set the ocean alight.

Patrick Dunsmore (13)
George Heriot's School

I Saw...

I saw a football pitch covered in bones,
I saw a graveyard with frosted petals,
I saw early spring flowers playing violins,
I saw an orchestra dawning in the east.
I saw the sun exploding with a *bang!*
I saw some dynamite ringing out.
I saw a bell happily scream and shout,
I saw some children falling from the sky.
I saw the raindrops swimming in a tank,
I saw my goldfish making a boring speech.
I saw a Tory, winning an Oscar,
I saw an actor roaring on the plains.
I saw a lion eating from a dish,
I saw a cat fixing a car,
I saw a mechanic burning through space.
I saw an asteroid growing green leaves,
I saw a tree full of wonder,
I saw this sight and wept with joy.

Hugh R Brechin (12)
George Heriot's School

I SAW A STREAM

I saw a stream with leaping flames
I saw a fire with many names
I saw a tree in crushing pain
I saw death in heavy rain
I saw an umbrella flying with a bird
I saw a kite like a cat, absurd
I saw a lion in a dazzling white dress
I saw a dancer in a flower press
I saw a leaf, a vivid blue
I saw the sea with terrible flu
I saw a child howling aloud
I saw a wolf like a darkening cloud
I saw her frown upon a quay
I saw all that I could see.

Sarah Dewhurst (12)
George Heriot's School

TREE OF AGE

Young, weak saplings
trying, battling against
the wind, the rain -
Reaching for the sun.

Dreaming of summer,
meadows, scented evenings.
But the harsh real world
will make us grow.

I reached for the sun,
yearned for golden wings.
Before my roots became
so deep, too deep . . .

You blossomed first, giving
sharing sweet fruit.
Gentle flowers, my branches
were bare, gnarled and awkward.

But I simply admired
and quietly swayed in those
summer evenings. Silently
touching your leaves.

One day I will burst
forth with beauty and
grace. Stand beside you
stunning and awe-inspiring.

The landscape will change,
then you can lean over
to my fragile petals.
Whilst we creakily tell of
sweet summer meadows.
Fables of visiting birds and
tales of windy loves.

Heather O'Brien (16)
Inveralmond Community High School

HE!

Looks to kill, but heart of stone
A lover's quest is never done.
Brutally honest, painfully quick
Watch him chanting out his wit.

Society keeps up its pace
But watch him trample on the faith.
Too fast to live, too young to die,
But never a tear shows in his eye.

Playing with fire - his favourite game.
He is ruthless, has no shame.
Heaven is Hell in his mind
Seeks to find more of his kind.

Women come and women go
Love is nothing but a foe.
He mentions nothing of his trust
Only of his need for lust.

It seems to be, he has no fear
In constant fights throughout the year.
Stories which he must confess
Will be revealed after his death.

His luck continues to the end
And is himself his own best friend.
He has no guilt - it is a fact
Even when caught in the act.

He is the first and then the last
He speaks no truth about his past.
This poem speaks of no remorse,
Only of his strength and of his force.

Sally Grubb (15)
Inveralmond Community High School

MEMORIES

Early day memories come out of slumber,
A gripping pain of happy thoughts,
The ease of talk and truth.
A young me on a box,
Weeding, counting, being me
Free-flowing points of view.
No need to wear a mask to please,
Say truth to disapproval
Encouragement and understanding,
Silently shown.
Not till late do you miss
The previous privileges.
The weight of loss grows by day,
By night it wars as an illusion.

Claire Anderson (16)
Inveralmond Community High School

SHE KNOWS ALL ALONG

The felt darkness
with a shrewd blue stream of light
surround me.
I lie awake shivering
in fear, that fate
controls me,
The low nagging talk
of the freak in the corner
annoys me.
The slow thudding
of the time
dements me.
I turn on the light
- she made me do it
- she knew I would
trip over trip
- she toys with me.
Am I freaking out?
No! That's what she would like!
Ha! I can confuse her!
Or did she prepare for this already?
What do you want from me?
I scream aloud.
The wicked temptress of fate herself
falls upon me.
She's gotten to me.
I knew this would happen.
She knew this would happen,
And we knew I would write this,
And we knew you would read this!

Gillian Montgomery (16)
Inveralmond Community High School

ATROPHYING SOCIETY VALUES

This degeneration has a lack of emotion
Non-penetrative speeches without devotion
Reverse psychology, use it on yourselves
Runaway from your personality, I really did
I say 'I'm an armchair conspiracy theorist'
I can tell you're never impressed.
You cannot put me in a box because hate can
Break through any locks.
Forever held in a dead-end journey, needing to be myself.
Hate, what you have become to escape, what you hated being
Every hero you have will fade away - just like you will.
We all vent our spleens once in a while,
But maintain our velvet glove.
We are all decorated with characteristics
But most ostracise the useful ones.
Most are complacent and non-imaginative.
Emotions slowly atrophying
Become an ersatz of your enemies
And end up with a final omega.
Few are affable and most allow themselves to be spreadeagled.
You will soon notice your world is unequivocally mundane.
And this omega I speak of, is something you shame
And you have yourself to blame.
I deny this disease
I'm so full of hatred I'd give you my heart,
Feeling like a stone in the dirt
Learned now how to breathe on hurt.
As soon as you change, you become them
Everything you ever hated,
Then you will see you're better off . . . dead.

Leila Pryke (15)
Inveralmond Community High School

THE CORRIDORS

As you walk through the empty corridor
Throughout the school, there isn't a sound
Apart from the sounds of teachers speaking to their pupils.
The litter brushes off your feet,
Only one janitor is picking it up off the floor.

In the classes thirty wee faces looking up at the blackboard,
As the teacher goes on and on, without coming up for air.
You see it in her face and the tone of her voice.
How mush she enjoys the teaching ways,
But still the corridors are . . .

Bring! Bring! Bring! The bell sounds for break.
There's a rush for the door and the teacher sits down.
And all those wee faces get hurried and frowned
It's a race for the stairs and the Tuck Shop line.
As the teachers retreat for their den through the crowd.

Nobody apart from teachers knows what goes on behind those doors,
Do they have secret things like TVs, DVDs, computer games and more?
People think that teachers are smart, but poor,
We know about all the old dears,
Because all the corridors have secrets.

Harry Foster (16)
Inveralmond Community High School

DON'T LET GO

It hurts to hear the sadness in your voice
When you cry out in pain
It hurts to know you're losing the will to live
The hurt drives me insane

It kills me to see the position you're in
The clock ticks by, it's late
But keep on fighting until the end
It'll kill me to lose you to fate.

It cuts deep to know you won't be here forever
Guiding me through life
It'll cut deep when life takes you from me
Cut deep - with a cold-hearted knife.

But I know there's a place I'll be with you
I know cos my heart's that place
Where memories will show me a picture of you
And as always, a smile on your face.

But whilst you're still here, I'm taking advantage
I'm gonna hold you ever so tight
I'm sorry if you feel I never let go
I'm holding you with all of my might.

Fiona McAllister (15)
Inveralmond Community High School

NERVES!

The day has finally arrived
All my hard work will be put to the test,
The nerves begin to take over
Can I face up to my challenge?

We finally arrive at the alley
People are on the lanes.
I then begin to wonder
Will I be able to do the same?

I finally have to go down on to the lanes,
We all type in our names.
My legs begin to shake with nerves,
I feel like a slithery snake.

A smile comes over my face,
I see the scoresheet upon the wall.
My heart is filled with joy
'Top ten!' I say, I jump with glee.

I now look back
Why was I nervous again?
If I could do it today, then
Next time, no problem!

Claire Robson (16)
Inveralmond Community High School

CHANGE

People say nothing changes!
But I know a lot has changed.
Especially my friends
I have seen war, death and life
But the worst I have seen, is terrorism.

I ask my family why?
But they don't know!
I am scared for their lives
As well as for mine.

I wish nothing would change,
I know that it has to change
Life is precious . . .
And so are memories.

Robert Connor (13)
Inveralmond Community High School

A PRAYER

This is a prayer
for Pat
an old friendly
man
who lived round
the back

He used to be my
babysitter
when I was a boy.
But now the only thing
that's left of him
is memories of all the joy.

The thing that I have
learned from this is
you don't know it's there
till it's missed.
So if there is a God
up there,
This one is special,
look after him,
and take care.

Michael Dickson (13)
Inveralmond Community High School

What Are We Like?

I thought I saw in the moonlight
A dove, bright as bright,
Its flappy wings, its sleek tail
It hardly makes a shrieking wail.

A teacher shouts, but it's not their pleasure,
It's not as if they are at leisure.
A teacher may not look like a wild animal,
But it does eat them, as a cannibal.

When I think of writing a poem up,
I try to do so with near me a cup.
I start to write, I stop to wish,
I work through it, just to finish.

Nicholas Shaw (13)
Inveralmond Community High School

THE MAN WHO WAS...

There used to be a man I knew
A man, loving and caring
A man who was there for me
A man who stood in as a dad for me
I guess I took him for granted

One day, he was gone
I asked my mum 'Where is he?'
She said 'On holiday, but never to return'
'Where has he gone, Turkey?
Greece, Spain or Rome?'
'No!' She said 'Heaven'

The man with the woolly jumpers
The man with the warm heart
The man with the lovely songs
The man who was my grandad.

Hilary Mackay (13)
Inveralmond Community High School

FRIENDS

Small friend
Big friend
Whoever it is
As long as they're a friend
Trustworthy, helpful, care for you
If they have all of these then,
They're a friend for you.

John Batt (11)
Inveralmond Community High School

I STARTED THAT DAY

I'm up, I'm dressed
but, my head is in a mess
maybe I'll look dumb
or displaced
I start the new school today

I've packed my bag
I'm in the car
Mum says 'You look like a star'
I start the new school today.

I'm in the office, sitting with Mum
I can't talk, I can't walk
In comes the Head, to see how I am
He has to start the new school today

I walk to class with Mr McGhee
The bell rings, everyone looks at me!
I've started the new school today.

Five weeks have passed
I've made new friends
But every day I wonder
About the new Head
I hope he enjoys his new school
The one he started that day.

Laura Cairns (12)
Inveralmond Community High School

FRIENDS

My best friends are fighting
They shouted 'Alan!'
I said 'What?'
They said -
'Let's go away from that keech!'
They were playing football.

When we went in, I said
'I'm going to write a poem
The poem will be called . . .
I haven't got one best friend,
I've got five!'

My friends like football
My friends are good runners.

Alan Rooney (11)
Inveralmond Community High School

CONSEQUENCES

At school, I had English
She said I'd done well
Then, the fire bell!

Out of school
In a swarm
Someone's set off the alarm!

We got in a line
The Fire Brigade came
But - somewhere else -
Someone was burning.

The brigade went to the house
But, there was nothing left
Not even a mouse.

Two children and their mother
They died - in the fire.
So take care, for the
Consequences could be dire!

Jamie Fairley (11)
Inveralmond Community High School

BABY

She can be a pain
But, she's got a smart brain
Her name is Claire
She sounds like a bear
And
She's a pear
As you walk
Behind her
On the stair
She
May be a little rotter
But she smells like butter.
Her room?
Well, it's a clutter.

Stacey Burns (11)
Inveralmond Community High School

MY FRIEND

The first day I came to school
I met this girl called Hilary
She always smiles and makes
Everybody happy.
She is a caring, sharing friend
And everybody loves her.
I am glad she is my friend
After school, we muck around.
We phone each other only if we're
Stuck on homework.
She is always there for you,
To help or to talk to.
That is why she is my pal.

Leah Kelly (13)
Inveralmond Community High School

ABOUT MY UNCLE

There he was just lying there
not even moving.
Sometimes it looked like he was dead,
but I knew he wasn't.
Sometimes he would turn around
and just look at me and smile.
Then he would not say anything
for a while, then he would
wait until everyone was out of the room
then he would always shout for a drink.

Ami Reid (13)
Inveralmond Community High School

REFLECTION

I am trapped in a body with no reflection
I shout and shout but no one hears my cries,
I sit in my room with nothing to do.
Oh! Why can no one hear my cries.

I go outside to look around
Look at what the world has.
There's life in the world, but no one sees
But I do, but no one cares.

I had a dream one night
There were people, lots of people
But no one noticed me
I had no reflection.

What can I do in a world that does not see?
Where I can't be heard!
I may as well not be here
This way, I don't need to suffer.

Goodbye cruel world
I don't have to suffer
I am invisible
I have no reflection.

But wait! I can be heard
These people don't hear, but someone will
I will start again, a new life
I will be seen. I will be seen.

Ian Munro (13)
Inveralmond Community High School

THE BIG HOLE

There he was
lying in the hospital bed,
Smiling, laughing
as if he was okay.
But he wasn't!
I could tell
'Here's a mint' he'd say.
I took one from the bag
his hands were shaking
as if he was scared.
But inside, so was I,
Scared that he might be gone.
Snatched away, disappeared
I was there the next day
to hear his laughter to see his smiles.
But his smiles and his laughter were there no more,
For he had gone to a better place.
But still I have a hole inside,
A hole that used to be filled with the joy
of a loved one.
I long to hear his laughter and see his smiles again.

Jemma Gilchrist (13)
Inveralmond Community High School

THE LESSON

My laughter withdraws
My heart no longer beats
My body fails to function.

As I am late
I will pay
I enter but something is wrong
The teacher, as happy as a child with toys,
Welcomes me to the class.

I am terrified
My fate awaits me
The face of the teacher is as alien to me
As Hannibal's elephants to the Romans
Her joy fills the air
She lights up the room.

Things will never be the same
She's now a different person
But I will never know
What happened before 'the lesson'.

Michael Ashby (13)
Merchiston Castle School

BELIEF

It lies at the end of the corridor,
Untouched
Unwanted
Just there!

I creep up slowly,
Scared
Cautious
Pondering my destiny.

I move along the bewildered row
Slower
And slower
Imagining what lies within.

Now reaching out
Thinking
Believing
I can! I can!

I did!

Jonathan Paterson (14)
Merchiston Castle School

THE HARE

Receding view,
The leveret sees
His mother bounding through the grass
To find the day's four meals.

Sit tight she seemed to say,
And do not move,
For everything will see you as
Just a tuft of grass.

As she makes her way
Her eyes a dead hare perceive,
It's body rotted by the winter rains.

A fox she sees on the prowl,
Skirting the ridge of the hill,
He is thin through lack of food,
But looks for easier meals.

As she's bounding through the wheats
She thinks of summer,
The easy life for all.

Dusk is near and she must now
Return to feed her young.

She makes her way towards the ground,
Which this morn she left,
She finds him, licks him,
Wakes him up
And takes him out to feed.

It now is dark
She snuggles down
With her young drawn near.

They, now together, look just like
The next hummock of grass.

Matthew Hardcastle (14)
Merchiston Castle School

THE FIGHT

I remember the pain
Pain
The pain of being hit so hard,
As the blow sinks in so far,
And fading
Fading.

I remember the anger
Anger.
Anger building up to an abnormal stature,
Trying to remain calm and mature,
And failing
Failing.

I remember fighting back
Fighting.
Letting go of all self control.
Flailing my fists and punching my soul
And losing
Losing.

I remember the blood
Blood.
Blood pouring out of my nose,
Soaking my hands and my clothes
And fainting
Fainting.

I remember waking up
Waking
Feeling a dent in my shape,
My lip covered in a thin strip of tape

And living.

Living.

Neil Campbell (13)
Merchiston Castle School

THE GEORDIES

As they leave their houses
By the thousands
Some in shirts, some in scarves.
They cross the Tyne Bridge
Singing songs of 'the magpies'.

The greatest group of fans in the
World sing, so louder than the visitors
However drunk they are,
A place for heroes
Such as Keegan and Shearer.

As the game gets underway
The boys begin to play,
From left to right, and right to left
They play the game they love.

Andrew Knox (13)
Merchiston Castle School

THE CAT

The cat dreams in a time
That no one will know except him.
For this is his time now
Not his owners, just his.

He sleeps in a curled ball of fur,
His chest gently moving up and down.
His mind is empty of unwanted thoughts,
Just a pleasant dream of peace.

He sleeps on his bed, next to the fire,
His fur shining like the orange dew of dawn.
And his head is protected
By his paw-pad of leather.

He awakes from his unspoiled dream,
Not recognising any of the frantic actions
Of the people around him,
And keeping his cool posture,
He closes his eyes to await his next reverie.

Oliver Rodi (13)
Merchiston Castle School

ISLAND

I step onto the beach
The sun beating down on my back.
The sand fine and warm creeping in-between my toes,
And the sea crumbling onto the shore.

I reach the first line of trees
They sway in the wind.
I enter and crunch through the foliage,
And hope not to disturb a soul.

I follow a dingy path
I stumble through a spider's web,
It clings on to my face
And almost holds me back, but I trundle on.

At points, the sun seeps through the treetops,
I look up to catch the blue tint of the sky.
Before I return to the depths of the gloom
My eyes are dazzled and blurred.

It is like another world, and dark
I ponder on where I am
I'm like an explorer in a new world,
But also lost!

Michael Black (13)
Merchiston Castle School

OCEAN FURY

As the wind howled through the rigging,
And the sea crashed down the decks,
The crew dodged between the waves
Trying vainly to negotiate the ship whilst remaining dry.

Even when the sea was calm,
The waves reached up to the deck,
Still posing a threat to the unwary sailor,
Thus the sea's treachery in all her moods.

It was so cold, that there was a man
Stationed permanently to chip ice off the bridge.
Five men were found frozen at their positions
And at a watch's end, all limbs were rigid.

The Corvette was escorting a vital convoy
In the North Atlantic ocean,
Where the sea was permanently below zero
For this was the dreaded Murmansk run.

Adam Clark (13)
Merchiston Castle School

A CONFESSION

Forgive me
For it was I
Who rang your bell
Then ran away

The tousled head
Was mine,
That peeked from behind the bush,
Which of course, I regret.

However, you must admit
You did look a sight,
You surely can't blame me for my laughter,
Which I probably regret . . .

Forgive me
For I have lied
I am not one inch
Remorseful.

It was wicked . . .
It was brilliant
I had
The time of my life.

Unrepentantly yours,
          Anonymous.

Alasdair Hardie (12)
Merchiston Castle School

FORGOTTEN RELATIONSHIP

I have said goodbye
I confess I leave you
To enjoy myself for once
To read, without disturbance
To enjoy tranquillity.

Tonight I shall go out
To a smart restaurant,
Have a G&T
With some friends
And enjoy my surroundings.

Tomorrow I shall awake
With the sun glittering
In my eyes;
However, I will not move
From my slumbering position.

Perhaps some day
We shall meet again;
But for now, you are
A memory
A distant, almost forgotten, memory.

Archie Millar (12)
Merchiston Castle School

A CONFESSION

This is just to say
I have eaten
The grapes
That were on the vine
In your back yard.

They had been growing
For many years
And were probably just ready
To be devoured.

They were so small
Round
Soft
And innocent.

Forgive me
These green grapes
Were also so flavourful
And scrumptious.

Hamish Locke (12)
Merchiston Castle School

A CONFESSION

I have taken
ten pounds
from the jar
in the kitchen.

'Why?' I hear you ask.
The truth is
that I wanted
to fill my wallet.

'What?' I hear you cry.
Yes, I know it was
an awful thing to do
but it was too tempting.

'How?' I hear you roar.
That crisp, new note
just lying there
I grabbed it and stuffed it
in my wallet.

Alastair Hall (13)
Merchiston Castle School

THIS IS JUST TO SAY . . .

I have to confess
Mr Wooley
I am very sorry

I was the one
who dangled
a chocolate biscuit

above the door
when you came
into the classroom
after your resolution

not to eat chocolate
for the next year.
I am sorry.
Sorry.

James Valpy (12)
Merchiston Castle School

A CONFESSION

He sat so cheerfully
with his fixed smile
in the shade of a plant

I could see
his innocent face
although some of it
was guarded by
his drooping hat

I know you
liked him
but he had to go -
I could not
resist

I squeezed the trigger
and *bang*
he was gone

I have collected
all the pieces
of your beloved
garden gnome

Please
forgive me.

Jon Watson (12)
Merchiston Castle School

A CONFESSION

This is just to say . . .

I have taken
your lamb
which was in
the paddock

and which
you were probably
saving
for lunch

I felt sorry
for him
all alone
in his paddock.

Forgive me
he was so lovely
so cute
and . . . so edible.

Josh Deery (11)
Merchiston Castle School

THE RAGING SEA

The raging sea swirls and hurls
The raging sea smashes against gigantic rocks
The raging sea goes back and forth with such power
It seems it will never cease.

The raging sea swells and pounds
The raging sea churns and foams
The raging sea destroys everything in its path
Remorselessly tearing down the land's barriers.

The raging sea is a threat to all
The raging sea is forceful and explosive
The raging sea takes no prisoners
But delivers all to the dark depths below.

Jonathan Gemmell (11)
Merchiston Castle School

KILLER

The biggest of all the cats,
The king of all the beasts.
With his powerful paws
And great strong head,
He's a force to win all wars.

The majesty of his eyes
And the swaying of his tail,
May lure a wandering deer,
Into the jaws of death.

He can run, jump, leap,
Dive, pounce and crawl,
But his ability to kill,
Is the most awesome thing of all.
The tiger.

James B Arbuthnott (11)
Merchiston Castle School

BLUE GIANT

Gliding through the silky ocean,
His huge bulk slowly moving to and fro,
He is, without doubt, king of the seas.
The other marine creatures,
Sharks, seals, dolphins and porpoises,
All are dwarfed by his sudden approach.
He is the blue giant.

Slowly he moves on to explore
The far reaches of
The blue desert ahead.
Then, gradually rises,
Rises to the ocean surface,
A tall fountain of spray
Heralding his approach.
Then he dives,
Back down into the deep.
He is the blue giant.

Leo J H Collins (11)
Merchiston Castle School

I WISH I WAS AN EAGLE

I wish I was an eagle
Who could fly so high
Away from war
Up into the sky

Away from school
Away from dangers
Away from the rooftops
Away from strangers

But if I was an eagle
I would fly away
From all those problems
Which come my way

But I'm not an eagle
I cannot fly away
I have to live as a human
As I was born to be this way.

Farooq Javed (10)
Merchiston Castle School

AUTUMN

Autumn means leaves fall down
You're all crumpling up now
You're getting red and maroon.
You've had your time but now it's time to go
It's autumn calling home, come home.
Next hot spring you can come back
And delight the trees with green, green leaves.

Lewis Deaves (10)
Merchiston Castle School

AUTUMN

Autumn leaves changing colour,
From green to orange to gold
And then the leaves start
F
a
l
l
i
n
g.

The autumn leaves
Lying thick and still,
In thick and bushy swarms.

When winter comes,
There are no leaves left on the ground,
In place of them there is shining, white
Snow.

Peter Singh (10)
Merchiston Castle School

THE WIDE OPEN SEA

On the beach,
Watching waves,
Up and down on a windy day,
Watching upon the wide open sea.

Boats crossing,
Speedboats racing,
Lots of things happening
On the wide open sea.

Charles Costello (10)
Merchiston Castle School

A PEAR

The shape of a light bulb
The colour of grass
Should smell of freshness
Is really all I ask.

To get one not mushy
Sometimes a hard task
Better when crunchy and juicy
Not solid like brass
Is really all I ask.

It should be mellow
And not too yellow, nae gas
For this good fellow
Is really all I ask.

James Henderson (11)
Merchiston Castle School

THE TIGGER MOVIE

Tigger is so *big*
He loves to bounce all day long
He's fat and fluffy.

Shelley McHale (11)
Newbattle Community High School

PARTIES

Dancing all night long
Good friends to joke and laugh with
Walking home alone.

Emma MacInnes (12)
Newbattle Community High School

CHRISTMAS

Christmas is here,
Can't wait to open presents,
I am excited.

Callum McLean (12)
Newbattle Community High School

THE SPOOK

The snake spooked the mouse
The mouse spooked the monkey off
The monkey spooked me!

Gary McNaughton (12)
Newbattle Community High School

TAURUS

Taurus is a star
Protective yet so cunning
And he's my star sign.

Nathan Rutherford (12)
Newbattle Community High School

PIZZA

Pizza is the best
With its fine, crispy, hard crust
And its cheesy base.

Shaun McNeish (11)
Newbattle Community High School

BEST FRIENDS

Best friends can listen
You can share all your secrets
They are very cool.

Stacey McCue (11)
Newbattle Community High School

SOUTH PARK

South Park is the best
Making you laugh at all times
Who killed poor Kenny?

Colin Haddow (12)
Newbattle Community High School

COCOA

Cocoa, thick and brown
Tasty, creamy, all year round
Cocoa, all gone, yum!

Louise Wilson (12)
Newbattle Community High School

THE WEE TEDDY BEAR

The wee teddy bear
Is sitting way over there
With cute little ears.

Neal Trainer (12)
Newbattle Community High School

FRIENDS FOREVER

Friends are nice and kind
They're always making me laugh
And they're special too.

Kerry Walker (12)
Newbattle Community High School

HALLOWE'EN

Hallowe'en is here
Oh Hallowe'en is fun
We spook everyone.

Callum Smith (11)
Newbattle Community High School

HOLIDAY

Sitting in the sun
Drinking chilled diet Fanta
Eating ice cream.

Samantha Ray (12)
Newbattle Community High School

HOLIDAYS

I like holidays
When there is something to do
If not it's boring.

Kelly Pryde (12)
Newbattle Community High School

THE HALLOWE'EN HAIKU

People are scared stiff
People get a fright tonight
It's darkness tonight.

Daniel Stuart (12)
Newbattle Community High School

CHOCOLATE

It's soft, dark and sweet
Just thinking about it, *yum!*
It's yum for the tum.

Robyn O'Brien (11)
Newbattle Community High School

MY DOG

My dog hurries to chew your feet,
He hurries to play with you
My dog tries to get attention
He tries to chew your fingers.

My dog lives in the kitchen
He is very furry
My dog is very hyper
Also very excited.

When my dog is very excited
He kicks and flips
He also runs very fast
And barks really loudly.

Bryan Monaghan (11)
St David's High School, Dalkeith

POEM ABOUT WINTER

Winter is cold
For the people who are old
It makes the trees look bare
I play the snowball fights I think are fair.

Robin's singing
Santa's bringing presents for everyone
But when winter's over
I scream with all my might
No more snowball fights.

Jamie Doyle (11)
Whitburn Academy

ROBIN IN WINTERTIME

Robin, robin, poor little robin
In the wintertime.
So hungry and poor
When the snow comes
It finds a barn on a farm
And tucks its head under its wing.

Mark Peebles (13)
Whitburn Academy

FRIENDS

Friends are loyal,
Friends are trustworthy,
Friends are secretive

And don't worry,
Friends understand.

They give a hand,
They want to have fun
And help everyone.

Kathryn Graham (11)
Whitburn Academy

STARS

The stars are just a big, bright light
When they show up big at night.

The stars are like a shiny jewel
Or a sparkle from a pool.

But how do we know what they are?
Well we just called them stars.

Stephen Kyle (12)
Whitburn Academy

Miss, Miss!

'Miss, Miss, he pulled my hair,
It's something that I just can't bear.
Miss, Miss, he hurt my foot
And then he went and stole my boot.
Miss, Miss, he called me names,
He said he was only playing a game.
Miss, Miss, he ripped my paper,'
'Oh, please dear, I'll deal with it later.'

Teirnie Miller (12)
Whitburn Academy

MY BEST FRIEND

My friend is honest and tells me all her secrets
My friend helps me when I am in trouble
My friend shares all her things
My friend is funny and makes me laugh
My friend is fun to be with
I am happy when I am with my friend.

Samantha Kellock (11)
Whitburn Academy

FRIENDS

F   riends are there to help you through
R   ound the bad and the good
I   f you fall out you always make up
E   ven when the times get rough
N   ever-ending, friends forever
D   ay to day we'll still be
S   taying friends forever.

Lynsay McShane (12)
Whitburn Academy

THERE'S NO PLACE LIKE HOME

There's no place like home
Being with your family.
There's no place like home
Playing in the garden.
There's no place like home
Sleeping in your own bed.
There's no place like home
Dreaming in your own room.
There's no place like home
Playing with your best friend.
There's no place like home
Eating home cooked meals.
There's no place like home
Being safe in the arms of the family.

Diane Malcolm (12)
Whitburn Academy

CLOUDS

Clouds are like
castles in the sky.

They look as if
you can bounce on them.

They look fluffy
as if they were candyfloss.

Stuart Wright (12)
Whitburn Academy

FOOTBALL

F   rom the kick-off we kick the ball
O   nside and offside
O   ut and in the sidelines
T   ear the opposition apart
B   all control is a legal part
A   ll the fans shout and roar
L   ook left and look right
L   ook again and score a goal, yeah!

Steven McCallum (11)
Whitburn Academy

MOONLIGHT

The moon pops up, when night crawls,
The moon makes sure day always falls.
The moon looks after us at night,
Until morning comes out as daylight.

If you look close enough you can see
A face smiling at you too!
Because the moon is your best friend
And always will be, no matter what!

Pamela Johnston (11)
Whitburn Academy

CHRISTMAS WILL COME SOON

Right now it is autumn
The leaves fall out of trees.
The leaves get swept away
By the cold winter breeze.
Soon it will be winter
The trees will be covered in snow.

My mum will get the car stuck
And then she'll have to get towed.
Then it will be Christmas Eve
I won't sleep a wink
Then Santa will come
And drink all his milk!

He'll creep to the fireplace
And wink his eye
And twitch his nose
And back up the chimney he goes.

Cheryl Fawcett (13)
Whitburn Academy

THE ELEPHANT

The elephant is big,
The elephant is huge,
It's the size of King Kong,
Its trunk the size of my dad.
It eats about a ton every day,
Its baby cuddles up and says
'Oh Mummy you're massive.'
The baby is as small as my little brother,
It roars all day as loud as anything,
It's massive.
My elephant is my *dad!*

Elaine Mill (12)
Whitburn Academy

MY BEST FRIEND

She's got long, blonde hair that shines like the sun;
Her blue eyes match the sky above;
She keeps my secrets when I tell them,
She's kind towards me;
She makes me laugh whenever I'm in a mood;
She's my best friend,
No one can change her.

Angela Bonnar (11)
Whitburn Academy

THE HAUNTED HOUSE

The broken doorknob as you enter the house,
No noise, not even the noise of a mouse.
The broken stairs are creaking,
A pipe upstairs is leaking.
The spider webs strung over each door,
The mess and broken chairs galore.
Outside the howling of a wolf sounds,
Quite near the large haunted house grounds.
The full moon outside in the sky,
The place deserted, no passers-by.
Blood stains covering the floors and walls
And on the shelves some porcelain dolls.
Then upstairs you open a door of black,
You see books of magic up in a stack.
Then you see the ghosts up there,
They won't even give you the chance to stare.
They'll grab you like a lump of lead
And within a few seconds you'll be dead.
Now I ask you the question, 'Do you want gore?'
Who would dare open the haunted house door?

Nancy Cook (12)
Whitburn Academy

MY MUM

I wake up in the morning, she is always there,
Even if she's hurt her leg and it is very sore.
Her favourite colours are lemon and aqua-green,
Her favourite food is pasta, disgusting it may seem.
She'd love to win the lottery or even go to Spain,
But she loves me every day, though I can be a right pain.
I'm wondering if I'll write any more,
But this little poem is for the person I adore.
This poem is for my mum of course, the cutest mum I see,
I'm now going to end this poem with a little buzzy bee.

Nikki Sked (12)
Whitburn Academy

OCTOPUS

O   n a night with the moon full
C   rawling steadily from the deep
T   o hunt, to play
O   n the surf a mystic shimmering
P   ulling closer to its goal
U   p and up till it sees another
S   o now it no longer sleeps alone.

Billy Sharp (12)
Whitburn Academy

BEST DAYS OF THE YEAR!

Christmas is the time of year
When people drink lots of beer.
Easter is a lot of fun
I hate it when the day is done.
Birthdays are the best of all
Growing older and getting tall.
These are the best days of the year
Living them is like drinking beer.

Lynne Charge (11)
Whitburn Academy

THE MOON

The moon is like a light,
A perfect circular light,
Like a car light coming and going,
Sometimes near, sometimes far,
Sometimes bright, sometimes dull,
Sometimes yellow, sometimes blue,
Most of the time the moon is white,
I'm looking forward to seeing the moon tonight.

Gary McKenzie (12)
Whitburn Academy

WINTER

In winter all the trees stand like bare skeletons,
Thin, crisp snowflakes fall slowly from the sky,
Most of the animals are hibernating,
Snow falling like soft balls of cotton wool,
Sharp thin icicles dripping from window sills,
Children running about, playing in the snow,
Families sitting down to Christmas dinner,
Exchanging gifts and cards,
Soon the snow will start to melt
And all the fun will be gone.

Amy Stewart (12)
Whitburn Academy

TUO EDISNI

The sea was green, the grass was red
All the living turned dead
Lions were purple, roses were blue
I was crying and so were you
I wanted to scream, I wanted to shout
Everything turned *inside out.*

David Paterson (12)
Whitburn Academy

WINTER NIGHTS

The street lights gleam on the white, white snow,
Through the snow the grass will grow.
Night goes by without a trace,
The morning sun rises full of grace.

Slowly the snow will fade
Children's happy feelings all away,
Once it was a lovely gleam
Now it's all a ruined dream.

Through the slush the children trod,
Without the snow it will be very odd.
The flying cloud, the frosty light,
The year is dying in the night.

Lauren Bonnes (12)
Whitburn Academy

A DAY I'LL ALWAYS REMEMBER

I was working in school when it happened
On the 11th of September
Only to see on the news that night
That day I'll always remember

My mouth fell open
I began to shake
As the gigantic tower
Crumbled like a quake

Through the sky
The flames roared
On the ground
Trapped people roared

Britain in shock
Devastation all round
On the 14th
For three minutes, no sound

George Bush made speeches
'It was an act of war,' he said
Even a pacifist's face
In anger would turn red

Why did they do this?
What did they achieve?
To kill is wrong
Don't they believe?

The 11th of September
A day I'll always remember.

Claire Cuthbert (15)
Whitburn Academy

MY MUM!

She's small, but big-hearted,
She helps me when I feel blue,
She has twinkling eyes like diamonds,
This full poem is true.

She's as sweet as sugar,
She always cares about me,
The best mum in the world,
Deserves a good cup of tea.

I love her being my mum,
Because she understands me,
I can't imagine the world without her,
As love from her is free.

She knows that
I'll love her always too
This she can't forget, for the simple reason
That mums like her are few

She is the best friend
In the whole of history
Even though she is my mum
Even to me it is a mystery

There are too many good things to say
That one poem couldn't hold
She's smart, funny, totally mad
And her heart is made of gold!

She is the best mum I could've asked for
On her I can depend
We will be best friends forever
Together 'til the end.

Lianne Cuthbert (13)
Whitburn Academy

THE BEACH

'Caw,' I hear another seagull screech.
What is so special about the boring beach?
When I was little I had my bucket and spade
But now I'm older and want an arcade.

I end up just sitting, nothing to do,
Then five minutes later, a ton of sand in my shoe.
What's the point of building a sandcastle?
If you ask me it causes more hassle.

I would go in the water but it's minging
Plus the jellyfish are stinging!

Just look at my mum and dad,
It's actually quite sad.
They are trying to get a tan,
When they're still as white as the Michelin Man.
But suddenly, everything seems better,
As though getting some heartfelt letter.

The sun rises more and more
And there is a lot less for me to ignore.
The sea seems to be much brighter,
Although my parents seem to be getting whiter.

It is only when I put the bad things behind me,
That I truly see,
Just how special the beach can be.

Barry Carty (13)
Whitburn Academy

STARLIGHT

S   parkling in the sky,
T   winkling way up high,
A   round the moon so bright,
R   adiant in the night.
L   ooking out my window,
I   nto the midnight sky,
G   azing at the stars,
H   igh into the night,
T   he stars are really lovely, always shining bright.

Danielle Rigby (12)
Whitburn Academy

BUTTERFLY

B   eautiful creatures
U   nder the sun
T   ransforming from a caterpillar
T   o a butterfly
E   ntering a new world
R   eleasing their wings
F   luttering about
L   ovely in every way
Y   ou are beautiful.

Rhona Allardyce (13)
Whitburn Academy

HAMSTER

H amsters are cute little pets
A nd have cute little beady eyes
M y hamster is brown and white it is also fluffy too
S ome hamsters may bite and some hamsters may not
T he ones I like best are friendly, cuddly and cute
E very hamster is different in many, many ways
R ound, fat or thin, I like them anyway.

Zara McMullan (13)
Whitburn Academy

At The Beach

I see children playing happily in the baking sun,
I hear the waves crashing loudly against the rocky shore,
I feel the cool, gentle breeze pushing lightly against my skin,
I feel the fresh sea air as I bask in the sun,
I taste the sweet strawberry ice cream as it dribbles slowly
down my chin.

Kirsty Lamprecht (13)
Whitburn Academy

SCARED

It was a dark and starry night,
When the girl entered the room.
Little known to her,
She is about to face her doom.

Her face full of terror,
As the light beamed.
Almost as quickly as she entered,
She left the room and screamed.

Sarah Rhind (13)
Whitburn Academy

SPRING

Small starlings sing in the sun,
In the bird bath splashing around,
Talking out loud like a mothers' meeting.

Flowers bright as the sun,
Swaying in the spring breeze,
Doing their dance in step.

The cat sleeping in the warm sun,
Having pleasant dreams on his rug,
Awaking with a yawn,
Now after some mice.

Spring is here to stay,
Spring will be here forever,
Spring is a happy time,
Spring is here.

Sarah Smillie (13)
Whitburn Academy

In The Classroom

As I sit in the class I can see -
Danielle brushing her hair,
Sarah chatting to Claire,
Zara raising her hand,
Frazer pinging an elastic band,
Gary laughing at a joke,
Richard taking a drink of Coke,
Nicola and Debbie talking,
Barry getting up and walking,
All going on while Mr Smith
And Miss Heenan are talking.

Elisa McGurk (13)
Whitburn Academy

DREAMING

Boldly going where you've gone before,
Through your head and onward more,
Down the stairs and through the door,
Until you reach your final floor!

You see your world through your eyes,
Where no one ever, ever dies,
No one cries and no one lies,
A perfect world where no one pries!

It never ends until you hear,
That beep, beep, beep in your ear,
I'm afraid that's when you fear,
The school bell is very near!

Sarah McCaig (13)
Whitburn Academy

THE MASTERS

I see all the famous golfers,
I smell the fresh morning air,
I hear the golf balls go zooming through the air,
I feel the golfer's hand as he shakes mine,
I hear my dad ask for his autograph,
I see Tiger Woods holing a thirty foot putt,
I hear the crowd clap and roar,
I smell the hot dog van behind me,
I see the last golfer finish the round,
I hear the winner's name getting announced,
I see him lift the trophy.

Gary Peebles (12)
Whitburn Academy

A SNOWY DAY

A white, snowy day
The crunchiness of the snow
Footprints everywhere.

Nicola Kellichan (13)
Whitburn Academy

OCTOBER

As I gaze up in the tree,
I see four million little leaves
Falling to the ground in the breeze.

When I wake up in the morning,
I look down on the grass.
It glistens in the morning sun,
Just like crystal glass.

I see dressing-up costumes in the shop window
I see children trick or treating
Just like clowns, laughing and eating.

Fraser Black (13)
Whitburn Academy